For:
Nicola and
Natalie,
Jonathan and
Stephen xx

This book was first published in 1990 by Princess House
an imprint of Studio Editions Ltd
Princess House, 50 Eastcastle Street
London W1N 7AP, England

Text written by Claire Nielson

ISBN 1 85170 336 5

Printed and bound Hungary

CHESTER AND MAX
BIG WORD BOOK

ILLUSTRATED BY JANE HARVEY

PRINCESS HOUSE
LONDON

"Come on Max, let's have fun!"
Calls Chester the Mouse,
"Let us label the things
We can see around the house."

Can you read the words too?
Why don't you try,
But Max needs some coaxing,
Perhaps he's just shy!

Cat

Chester writes out a word,
Saying "Here's what we do.
First you read the word **cat**
Then I'll tie **cat** to you."

Hat

Now the **hat** has a label,
And so has the mat,
But cat tied to Max – Oh,
He doesn't want that!

Mouse

Here nibbling his pencil
Sits a thoughtful small **mouse**.
There must be somewhere for
His latest word, house.

mouse house

House

Now he's found the right **house**,
Chester looks quite at ease
Leaning back on a fork
While he munches some cheese.

house

fork

mouse

Dish

Max sniffs at his food,
Lying there in his **dish**,
But Chester cries, "Wait!
We must label it fish."

Fish

Look out, greedy Max,
Take Chester's advice,
Eat the **fish**, not the label,
It just won't taste nice!

fish

dish

Game

Now our animal friends
Are planning more fun.
To find the best **game**,
They'll play with each one.

game

Ball

Chester's rolling around,
Trying hard not to fall.
How is Max going to label
That big bouncy **ball**?

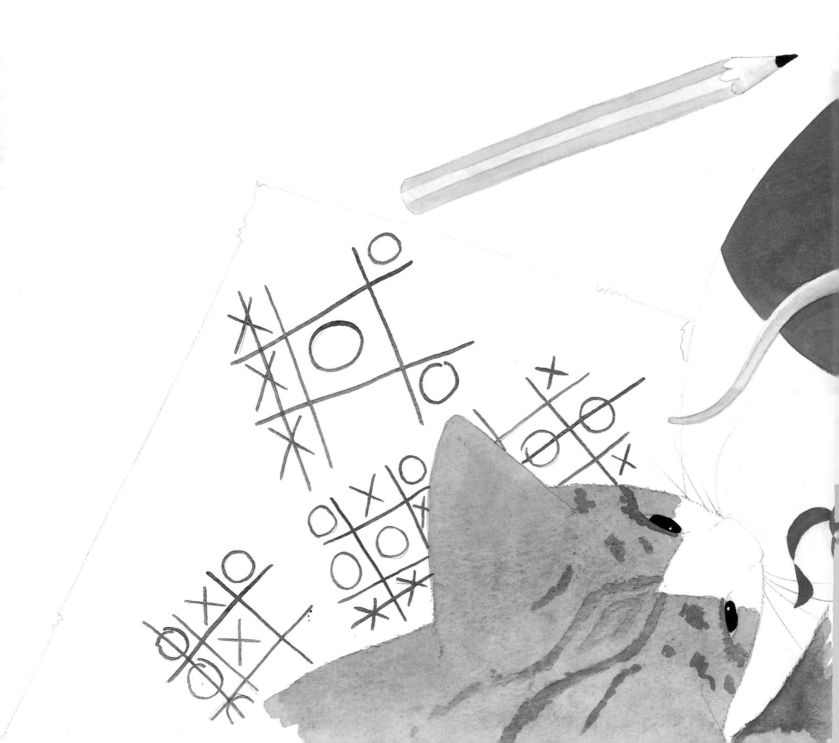

ball

game

Kite

Max tries hard to read
But the word's out of sight.
Behind him is flying
A red and white **kite**.

Kite

Balloon

Max has labeled the kite,
Not a minute too soon,
But what's tied to Chester –
He's not a **balloon.**

Kite

balloon

Toy

Chester needs help from Max
To play the next game.
As they look at each **toy**
They'll give it a name.

ball

toy

Teddy

A big handsome **teddy**,
Mouse, duck, doll and ball.
A rabbit, a tiger,
Can you name them all?

Ant

This **ant** word is easy,
And gives Chester a clue
For a word that's much bigger,
Max can't guess – can you?

Elephant

Elephant, elephant,
Each stands in a line.
Max reads this long word,
Yes, he's doing just fine.

elephant

Frog

Here's a funny green **frog**;
Chester winds its big key,
Let's see who the winner
Of this race will be.

frog

Dog

Chester jumps up and down
As he cheers on the frog,
But look out for the cat
Who is pushing that **dog**.

frog

dog

Parrot

Now what is the name
Of this colourful bird?
Max calls out the letters,
Chester writes down the word.

Carrot

The **parrot** says **carrot**,

Then says it again.

Max reads both these words

And gets ten out of ten.

Pen

"Clever Max!" Chester cheers,
"You must try to write now.
Here's a **pen** and some ink
And I'll show you how!"

Ink

Max writes **ink** and pen
But, oh dear, can you guess
Who's left Chester behind
In a black, inky mess?

Soap

The cat and the mouse
Soon wash themselves clean.
Though they use lots of **soap**
You can see where they've been.

Bubble

Chester's blowing a **bubble**,
He can't seem to stop.
When Max tries to name one,
The bubble goes – Pop!

duck

soap

bubbles

Clock

While Max tries to find
A place to tie clock,
Chester gets busy
First with **tick** and then **tock**.

CLOCK

Tick Tock

They've written two labels,
And tied one to the clock,
But neither are able
To label **tick tock**.

1
2
3
4
5

clock

tick

Spoon

Chester writes by the light
Of the silvery moon.
Max knows what the dish
Ran away with – the **spoon**.

Spoon

Moon

Max has the right label,
He's tied spoon to spoon.
Chester can't stretch his paws
To tie **moon** to **moon**.

mat	ink	frog
dog	hat	tick-tock
mouse	duck	clock
parrot	cat	kite
dish	doll	ant
toy	fish	soap

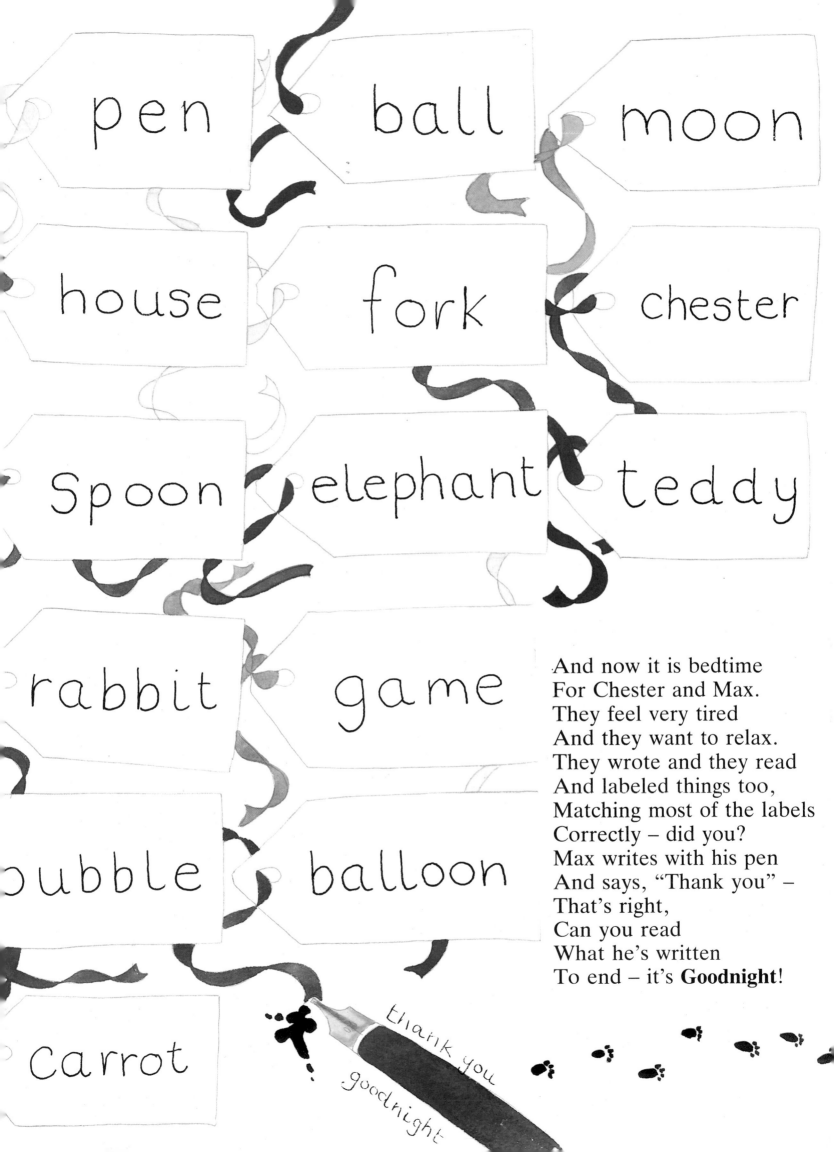

pen

ball

moon

house

fork

chester

Spoon

elephant

teddy

rabbit

game

ubble

balloon

carrot

And now it is bedtime
For Chester and Max.
They feel very tired
And they want to relax.
They wrote and they read
And labeled things too,
Matching most of the labels
Correctly – did you?
Max writes with his pen
And says, "Thank you" –
That's right,
Can you read
What he's written
To end – it's **Goodnight**!

thank you

goodnight